LITTLE PIG'S PICNIC
AND OTHER STORIES

WALT DISNEY STORY BOOKS

HERE THEY ARE

DONALD DUCK AND HIS NEPHEWS

WATER BABIES' CIRCUS AND OTHER STORIES

PINOCCHIO

DONALD DUCK AND HIS FRIENDS

LITTLE PIG'S PICNIC AND OTHER STORIES

MICKEY NEVER FAILS

SCHOOL DAYS IN DISNEYVILLE

(Listed in order of difficulty)

LITTLE PIG'S PICNIC
AND OTHER STORIES

Told by

MARGARET WISE BROWN

Illustrated by

THE WALT DISNEY STUDIO

D. C. HEATH AND COMPANY
BOSTON

D. C. HEATH AND COMPANY

NEW YORK   BOSTON   CHICAGO

ATLANTA   SAN FRANCISCO   DALLAS   LONDON

STORIES IN THIS BOOK

THE LITTLE PIG'S PICNIC

Once upon a time in a barnyard there was a tiny little pig. There were eight little pigs and two big pigs, and there was a tiny little pig. Her name was Squeaker.

Squeaker was a runt pig, a very little pig. But her appetite was big.

It was as big as the appetite of a big pig. But poor little Squeaker, she did not get much to eat.

Every time old lady pig rolled over on her side to feed her little pigs, Squeaker would get pushed away. Squeaker would push and nudge, but the other little pigs would not budge. Not for such a little runt. Not for Squeaker!

"Oink! Oink!" Squeaker jumped up and down on the outside.

"No room! No room!" squeaked the little pigs. And poor little Squeaker was left out in the cold. She could not get anything to eat.

So off went Squeaker, all through the wide barnyard, to look for her supper.

First she came to the pond where the swans were feeding. She sat down on her little pig seat on the bank and watched them. The swans floated over the water. Then quickly their heads darted down the full length of their necks into the water. They seemed to be eating something.

"Oink! Oink!" said Squeaker. "There must be something good down there. Nothing is too good for this little pig!"

So down Squeaker splashed into the water after a swan supper.

But a pig is not a swan. And Squeaker could not swim. Just in time to save her from drowning, the old mud turtle rose from the bottom of the pond like an island underneath her. And Squeaker rested on his shell.

"Little pig, little pig," said the old mud turtle, "go back and find a little pig's supper. This is no place for you. Get away from this pond and go find a pig's supper!"

So, with a wiggle and a shake, off went little Squeaker again. Off she went to hunt for her supper.

She looked at the geese by the pond.

She looked in the fields at the grazing sheep.

Then, she looked in the barn and saw old Bossy Cow.

Old Bossy Cow was feeding her little bull calf. There must be something good in there for a little pig's supper. So Squeaker jumped up and down underneath old Bossy Cow.

"Oink! Oink!" said Squeaker. "Nothing's too good for this little pig!"

> "By the two little holes
> In my little pig nose,
> Milk would be good
> For this little pig!"

But squeal and jump as she would, the milk was too far away. And the little calf mooed right in her face.

"Little pig, little pig," said old Bossy Cow, "go and find a little pig's supper. You will never be able to reach as high as a calf!"

"Oink, oink, oink," sighed Squeaker and trotted out of the barn. She was so hungry!

And off she went, all through the wide barnyard, to look for her supper.

Just then Squeaker heard a man's voice calling, "Here piggy, piggy, piggy!"

And Squeaker thought:

"By the two little holes
In my little pig nose,
That must mean
A little pig's supper!" x

And she ran and she ran till she came to the trough where the hogs were eating. The mother pig was there, too, and the little pigs were all there with her.

Squeaker ran right over the backs of the baby pigs. She jumped up on the edge of the trough.

But an old hog said, "Ugh! Ugh! There's no room here for a baby pig. No room! No room!"

And Squeaker was rooted right out
of there and sent squealing across the
yard.

Then down by the chicken house
she saw a big red dish of yellow
corn meal. "Oink!" said Squeaker.
"That looks good to this little pig."

> "By the two little holes
> In my little pig nose,
> There's a corn meal supper
> For this little pig!"

8

She ran right over to the pan and stuck her little pig nose in the corn meal. She knocked all the little feathery chickens away. Such a noise as they made! "Peep! Peep! Peep!"

The old mother hen came running with her beak wide open.

"Cluck-cluck! Ker-chuck!"

Squeaker didn't wait any longer. She started running away.

She knew there was no room in the chicken yard for this little pig.

Squeaker ran and ran all through the barnyard.

She watched the horses eat grass.

She watched the birds eat seeds.

She watched the donkey eat hay.

She watched the rooster eat worms.

But there was no supper for a little pig.

Poor little Squeaker! She ran all through the wide barnyard until she bumped into the corn crib. Bang! She knocked away the stick that held the door shut.

Down fell the corn! Down fell the golden ears of corn all over Squeaker. They tumbled in a golden pile around her. This was the little pig's picnic!

Then all the little chickens came running to the little pig's picnic.

The donkey brayed,
The rooster crowed,
The little colt neighed,
The little calf mooed,
And the oxen lowed
For the little pig's picnic!

And Squeaker ate and ate and ate and ate, there in the middle of the corn.

"Cock-a-doodle doo!"

THE BARNYARD SONG

The rooster began it
Early in the morning.
Before the sun's dawning,
The rooster began
The Barnyard Song.

And the little birds
Carried it along:
"Sweet wheat! Sweet wheat!"
"Cock-a-doodle doo!"
"Cluck, cluck, cluck!"
The chickens chimed in, too.

"Baa," sang the little lambs.
"Oink," sang the pig,
"I'll sing 'Ugh, ugh, ugh,'
When I get big."

"Sweet wheat! Sweet wheat!"
"Cock-a-doodle doo!"
"Moo, moo, moo!"
The cow joined in, too.

"Maa, maa, maa!"
Sang the little brown calf.
And the old gray donkey
Hee-hawed a laugh

To make a Barnyard Song.
And the small birds
Carried it along:
"Sweet wheat! Sweet wheat!"

And the big birds, too,
Until the old owl
Ended the song,
"To whit, to whoo!"

15

THE LONELY LITTLE COLT

When dawn came in the barnyard, the little colt was still asleep. His mother nudged him with her nose until she had him on his feet.

The colt shook himself and looked out of the window. But he shook himself too hard. He hadn't been in the world long enough to know how hard a colt should shake himself. His legs were not yet very strong. So down he went on his knees. But soon he was on his feet again and giving stiff little jumps on his brand new legs. His mother watched him with pride and joy.

He ran with his mother out of the barn and into the fields. Once around the field they galloped. Twice around the field they galloped.

Then the farmer came to the field. He whistled to the mother horse. And he said, "It is time for you to go back to work." He said, "You have galloped around with your baby long enough. Now you must help me cut a field of clover to make some hay."

Then the farmer took the mother horse away from the field. The little colt was left there all by himself.

At first the little colt wasn't very happy. He had never been left by himself before. And he did not like it. He galloped around close to the fence and neighed for his mother. Then he just galloped around the field faster and faster.

After a while he began to enjoy himself. He felt the warm sunshine. He smelled the green grass. He went to the fence and watched some geese march by. He wished the geese were

big enough to play with. But he couldn't gallop around the field with a goose.

Then the old gray dog came dashing across the field.

"The dog can run with me," thought the little colt. With a kick of his heels, he galloped after the dog.

But the dog would not wait to play that day. He ran right across the field and under the fence where the little colt couldn't go. The old gray dog was going to the hill to take care of the sheep. He didn't have time to play with a little colt.

Then the little colt saw a little pig running down the road. He ran over to the fence and neighed to the little pig. But the little pig only squealed and ran away. He was looking for something a little pig could eat. He did not want to play with a little colt.

Then the colt saw a sleepy little calf looking over the fence. The little colt ran over to the calf and stopped. Here was an animal his own size. They rubbed noses.

The little colt kicked up his heels.
The little calf kicked up his heels.

Then the little colt neighed.
Then the little calf mooed.
The little colt stiffened his legs and jumped.
The little calf stiffened his legs and jumped.

21

After that they seemed to feel that they knew each other. So they ran up and down beside the fence.

The calf ran up and down on his side of the fence.

And the colt ran up and down on his side of the fence.

Then a little boy came and opened the gate, and the colt rushed into the field with the calf. Soon they found another gate open. So they both ran into the farmyard and jumped over everything they saw.

They jumped over a chicken.

They jumped over a cat.

They jumped over a pig.

And they jumped over the bull.

They jumped and they jumped and they jumped.

And then when evening came, the mother horse whinnied and the colt ran home.

And the mother cow mooed and the calf ran home.

All this happened the day the colt and the calf came to know each other. After that the little colt was not lonely any more.

THE UGLY DUCKLING

Once upon a time there were two ducks. They had their nest on the edge of a pond in a far corner of the world. In the nest were five round, smooth eggs.

When the mother duck wasn't sitting on the nest, the father duck was sitting on the nest. All the time they were waiting for some little ducklings to come out of the eggs.

They waited for a long time. The
father duck walked up and down. He
walked up and down so much that he
wore a deep path in the earth where
he walked.

And then, one day, there came a
pick-pick-pick from inside the eggs.
And, one by one, out tumbled four
tiny yellow ducklings. When they
came tumbling over the edge of the
nest, the father duck looked at them
with pride and joy.

Then there came a pick-pick-pick from the inside of the fifth egg!

Out tumbled the fifth duckling!

There he stood on one foot. He did not look like the others. His feathers were white instead of yellow. His neck was longer. His eyes were big and staring.

When the other ducklings saw him, they ran and hid under their mother's wing. The mother duck stood there and looked. Never had she hatched a duck like this before.

The father duck came running with a quack-quack-quack.

"Where did this little thing come from?" he asked.

"You must have laid that egg," said the mother duck.

"I don't lay eggs!" said the father
duck. "Quack-quack-quack! Where
did this little thing come from?"

The little thing stood there with a piece of eggshell on his head like a hat. He looked around him for the first time at the brand new world. He was so very happy to be born. He looked at the tall green grasses and the pink water lilies of the world he was to live in. He did not know he was an ugly duckling.

Then the mother duck took her little ducklings for their first walk. She shooed the little yellow ducklings on before her. The little ugly duckling came waddling along behind. But when he tried to come close to the mother duck, she shooed him away.

"You're no child of mine," she seemed to say. Still, the little ugly duckling tagged along.

When the ducklings went for their first swim, the ugly duckling paddled his legs under him right along with the others.

"Well!" said the mother duck. "The thing is a swimming bird. But he certainly is a funny duck. Come, little ducklings, climb on my back."

The little ducklings climbed on her back with a "Quack! Quack! Quack!"

The ugly duckling swam very fast and climbed on too. Then the ugly duckling made his first noise.

"Honk! Honk!" he said.

What a strange noise for a duckling! The mother duck and the little ducklings ducked their heads. Who ever heard of a honking duck! They pushed the ugly duckling off the mother duck's back into the water. A duck who honked did not belong to them.

Then the mother duck and her ducklings all swam off and left the little ugly duckling diving around by himself. He was very lonesome.

The poor little duckling swam around by himself until he was tired. Then he climbed up on the dry land.

Sitting there, he looked down into the dark green water. There in the water was his reflection, all twisted by the water of the stream. He did not look like the other ducklings. His eyes were too big and his neck was too long. His feathers were white instead of yellow.

And then he knew. He was an ugly duckling. Big tears came out of his eyes and fell there on the ground.

Poor little duckling! Another big tear squeezed out of one eye.

He was not wanted. He was an ugly duckling, and nobody loved him.

So he wandered off all alone through the marshes — one little duck in the wide, wide world.

He only looked back once at the yellow feather backs of the other ducklings as they ran after their mother. Then he went away all by himself.

As he walked along, he did not see that the rushes grew green by the bank, and red-winged blackbirds were singing there in the sunlight.

Suddenly he heard a chirping. Looking up, he saw four friendly little marsh birds chirping to him from a nest in a fallen tree.

The ugly duckling gave a little honk and climbed right up into the nest with them. The baby birds chirped lovingly around him. The nest was warm, and the little birds were soft beside him.

33

All at once the little birds opened
their bills, and along came flying the
old marsh bird who was their mother.
She had a big worm which she threw
to them for their supper.

But when the ugly duckling caught
it, the mother bird squawked with
rage and pulled the worm away.

She chased the duckling from her nest, and pecked him on the head and beat him with her wings.

The little duckling ran and ran until he jumped into the water. Then he swam away as fast as he could. He went swimming so fast that he bumped right smack into a wooden duck, and started it to rocking.

When the ugly duckling saw the big wooden duck rocking there on the water, he rubbed his little head against the duck's wooden breast.

He did not know that it was just a wooden duck painted in wild-bird colors. He did not know that the wooden duck was put there by hunters to bring other wild ducks where hunters could shoot them.

He just thought, "Here is a friend."

The wooden duck did not swim away from him. Instead it let the ugly duckling climb up on the end of its tail and bounce up and down there.

He was so happy that he gave a big bounce in the air that landed him in the water. This tipped the wooden duck so far forward that when it rocked back again, it smacked the little duckling on the head.

This all happened the way a wooden

duck rocks on the water. But the ugly duckling thought his new friend had done it to him on purpose. And he swam off down the stream, the saddest little duck in all the world.

He hid in the reeds by the river and honked as though his little heart would break. His tears fell into the water and made little circles there. He stopped to watch one tear hit the water. Then he put his head down on the ground and cried and cried.

Just then a great white mother
swan and her four little swans came
floating down the river.

They stopped and listened when they heard the little duck honking there on the shore. And when the little swans saw the ugly duckling with his head down on the ground, they came swimming over to him.

"Honk! Honk! Honk!" the swans called to him.

When he heard them, the ugly duckling looked around and saw them there — four baby swans. They were as white as he was, and they all had long necks like his own. They were honking to him in a friendly way. He was so happy he dove right into his own reflection there in the water and broke it.

When he came up, the little swans were still there.

The young swans played with him
and swam in circles around him.

Then the great white mother swan
honked to the little swans. And the
ugly duckling looked up and saw her
there. Never had he seen such a
beautiful great white curving bird.
Never had he seen such whiteness
before.

The baby swans all went swimming
back to the great white swan. The
little duckling watched them go.
He wished he might grow up to be
beautiful like these swans. Then he
remembered he was an ugly duckling.
His little head dropped and he started
to swim off by himself, all alone on
the wide waters of the stream.

But the swans would not let him go. They knew that the ugly duckling was really a baby swan who had been hatched in the wrong nest. So the white swans swam round the little lost swan and stroked his neck with their beaks. The mother let him come near to the soft swan's down on her breast. Then she put her wing over her little lost baby swan and swam with him down the stream.

PLUTO'S CHICKS

Pluto was a funny dog. He should have been a mother, because he liked little animals. But he was not a mother. He was just old Pluto, the barnyard dog.

But one time he was just as good as a mother. He had a family of little yellow chickens. And they really were his family because they followed him everywhere he went. They thought that the old dog Pluto was their mother. And this is how it happened.

The old mother hen went into Pluto's dog house once while Pluto was away chasing rabbits. Pluto's dog house was full of warm hay. It was a fine place for laying eggs. So the old hen laid eggs in Pluto's house. She hid them under the hay and left them there.

When Pluto came home, he did not notice the eggs. He could not see them under the hay.

He was sleepy and tired, and so he curled himself up in his dog house and went to sleep.

For days and days the eggs lay under the hay.

One day while Pluto was asleep, the eggs under the hay began to hatch. And they hatched all over the place!

Crack! Crack! Crack! Out popped little yellow chicks all around Pluto, who was lying there sound asleep.

"Peep-peep, peep-peep!" chirped the little chicks.

They ran around Pluto, thinking that big old dog was their mother.

Pluto woke up with a jump. Never had anything like this happened to him before. He ran out of his house. And so did the little yellow chicks. They ran right after him, peeping as they ran.

Pluto hid behind a water trough. But the little chicks found him. Pluto hid in the horse's stall. But the little chicks found him there.

Pluto hid everywhere, but the little chicks always found him. And when they found him, they climbed all over him and they scratched around in the fur on his back.

Then, pretty soon, Pluto began to like being a mother. He walked proudly around the barnyard, with the little chicks at his heels.

When the little chicks scratched in
the soft ground for worms, Pluto
scratched too. With his big feet he
scratched a big hole, until the dirt
and the worms were flying through
the air. Then while the little chicks
went after the worms, Pluto lay down
to take a nap.

After a while, the old hen went down to Pluto's house to look after her eggs.

When she saw the hay covered with egg shells, she began to squawk, "My chick, chick, chicks! Where, oh where, are my chick, chick, chicks?"

She went rushing around, hunting for them everywhere.

"My chicks! My chicks! My chick, chick, chickens!" she squawked.

The old rooster heard her and he came running. The other hens heard her and they came running. The silly, squawking hens went running all over the barnyard until they came to the place where Pluto was watching the little chicks as they caught their first bugs. Pluto never looked up at them. He just watched his chicks.

But when the little chicks saw the old hen, they were afraid. They had never seen an old hen before. When she came running up to take them under her wing, they ran to Pluto.

They all huddled in the circle of his paw as he lay there. The old hen frightened them with her squawks. But Pluto just blinked at her over his little chicks. And the little chicks huddled together happily in the circle of his paw.

The rooster crowed, and the old hen squawked until she was tired. But the little chicks stayed with Pluto.

PLUTO'S KITTEN

Pluto was a cat hater. He chased every cat that he saw. He even chased every cat that he thought he saw. He dreamed about chasing cats at night.

And then one day Pluto came sniffing home and heard a noise in his dog house.

"Prrrrrr." A cat was purring in Pluto's dog house.

Pluto growled his deepest growl.

The yellow hair rose on his back. A cat in his dog house. SO! He went stalking in.

At first he couldn't see anything. But then, over in the corner, he saw a small black ball of fur. It was a very little ball of fur. But it had the biggest purr that Pluto had ever heard.

"Prrrr! Prrrrrr!"

The growl grew quiet in Pluto's throat. This little thing wasn't even big enough to growl at. It wasn't much bigger than a bug. Pluto didn't bite bugs!

Just then, the little thing saw Pluto. And that little black thing, that little fur bug, rose right up on its stiff little legs and spit at Pluto.

Pluto didn't know what to do. So
he went over in the corner of his dog
house and lay down. But he kept one
eye open and he watched that little
black kitten. And the little black
kitten watched Pluto.

Outside the dog house, night was coming all around like a big shadow. The little kitten was cold. And when it felt the warmth of Pluto so close, it came a little nearer.

All this time Pluto kept one eye open. The little kitten came closer. And the next thing Pluto knew, the little kitten had curled up there beside him and was purring in his ear.

That was how Pluto's little kitten came to him. And from that time on, wherever Pluto went in the barnyard, the little black kitten went, too.

THE GRASSHOPPER AND THE ANTS

"Oh, the world owes me a living,
    Tra la la lalala la."

The grasshopper was singing his
song as he jumped through the fields.
He almost jumped on top of some ants
who were pulling a grain of corn up
an ant hill.

Said the grasshopper to the ants:

"Why are you working
All through the day?
A summer day
Is a time to play!"

"We can't," said the ants. "Winter will soon be here."

The busy little ants did not have time to feel the warm summer sun, or to run and jump just for fun. From the beginning of day till the end, they were busy hauling the corn away. Winter was coming. They had no time to play.

All summer the grasshopper sang and danced his grasshopper dances in the grasses. When he was hungry, he reached out and ate.

And the grasshopper sang:

"The good book says:
'The world provides.
There's food on every tree.'
Why should any one have to work?
Not me!

Oh, the world owes me a living,
　Tra la la lalala la."

With that he took a big swig of honey from a blue harebell that grew above his head. Then he spit a big wet spit of grasshopper tobacco juice. It nearly landed on a little ant who was dragging a load of cherries to store in the ant house for the winter.

Said the grasshopper to the ant:

"The other ants can work all day.
Why not try the grasshopper's way?
Come on, let's sing
              and dance
                     and play!

Oh, the world owes me a living,
    Tra la la lalala la."

The little ant was so charmed by
the music that he dropped his heavy
load and started to dance.

Then came the queen, The Queen of All the Ants.

And The Queen of All the Ants frowned on the dancing ant so that he picked up his cherries and went back to the other busy ants. Then The Queen of All the Ants spoke sober words to the grasshopper:

"You'll change your tune
When winter comes
And the ground is white with snow."

But the grasshopper only made a
courtly bow.

"Winter is a long way off," he said.
"Do you dance? Let's go."

"Oh, the world owes me a living,
    Tra la la lalala la.
The other ants can work all day.
Why not try the grasshopper's way?
Come on, let's sing
              and dance
                and play!"

But even as he sang and played on his fiddle, The Queen of All the Ants hurried away. She, like the other ants, had no time to play.

All through the long lazy summer months the grasshopper went on singing:

"Oh, the world owes me a living,
    Tra la la lalala la."

There was no tomorrow. There was only today, and the sleet and the snow seemed far away.

But the little ants worked harder than ever. As long as the sun was in the sky, they went back and forth carrying the foods from the fields into their ant houses.

Then the winter wind began to blow. It blew the leaves off all the trees. The ants ran into their ant house and closed the door, and you didn't see them in the fields any more. Every day the winds would blow. And then one day, SNOW.

The grasshopper was freezing. He couldn't find any leaves to eat. All he had was his fiddle and his bow. And he wandered along, lost in the snow. He had nothing to eat and nowhere to go. Then far off he saw one leaf still clinging to a tree.

"Food! Food!" cried the hungry
grasshopper, and he leaned against
the wind and pushed on toward the
tree. But just as he got there, the
wind blew the last dry leaf away. It
fluttered away among the snowflakes.

The grasshopper dropped his fiddle
and watched the leaf go. It fluttered
away through the white snowflakes.
It drifted slowly away. It was gone.

And then he came to the house of
the busy ants. He could hear them
inside there having a dance. They
had worked hard all summer, and now
they could enjoy the winter.

The grasshopper was too cold to go
on. The wind blew him over, and he
lay there where he fell. His long
green jumping and dancing legs were
nearly frozen. Then very slowly he
pulled himself through the snow to
the house of the ants and knocked.

When the ants came to the door,
they found him there, half frozen.

And ten of the kind and busy ants
came out and carried the poor
grasshopper into their house. They
gave him warm corn soup. And they
hurried about, making him warm.

Then The Queen of All the Ants
came to him. And the grasshopper
was afraid, and he begged of her:

"Oh, Madam Queen,
  Wisest of ants,
  Please, please,
  Give me another chance."

The Queen of All the Ants looked
at the poor thin frozen grasshopper
as he lay shivering there. Then she
spoke these words:

"With ants, just those
  Who work may stay.
  So take your fiddle —

and PLAY!"

The grasshopper was so happy that his foot began beating out the time in the old way, and he took up his fiddle and sang:

> "I owe the world a living,
>   Tra la la lalala la.
>
> I've been a fool
> The whole year long.
> Now, I'm singing
> A different song.
> You were right,
> I was wrong.
>   Tra la la lalala la."

Then all the ants began to dance, even The Queen of All the Ants.

And the grasshopper sang:

> "Now I'm singing
> A different song.
> I owe the world a living,
>   Tra la la lalala la."

THE ORPHAN KITTENS

Three little kittens were once born into the world. One was black. One was white. One was a calico kitten. And when they felt the warmth of their own little bodies, they all began to purr. For they thought the world was wonderful.

They even thought that the mean old farmer who owned them was wonderful. And just as soon as they could crawl, they crawled all over his house. But the farmer did not like the kittens.

"One cat on a farm is enough," he said. "Get rid of those kittens. Throw them away."

So the farmer's son put the kittens in an old gunny sack and started for the river to drown them.

But the kittens thought the old gunny sack was wonderful, too. They rolled about in the darkness of the sack and wrestled and hugged each other. Then they curled up in a warm pile of fur and went to sleep.

They did not hear the farmer's son stop when he came to the river. They did not hear him say, "These little kittens might find a home if I carried them in to the town. I don't want to throw them into the river to drown. The river is too cold."

The three little kittens only woke
up when they were dumped from the
sack into a snowy garden. And that
was wonderful, too. They had never
before felt the snow under the cushions
of their little kitten feet. They did
not see the hand that held the gunny
sack disappear over the wall. They
did not know that they had been
thrown away into the white snow.

All that they knew was that the white snow was wonderful. They went creeping across it. Their bright little kitten eyes were shining like the stars in the night. The snow began to fall softly in the empty garden. The little black kitten batted it with his paw. And the other two kittens went pouncing after the soft snowflakes as they drifted toward the ground.

It was the little black kitten who
found the cellar door open. With
long leaps through the snow, the other
two kittens followed him in through
the open door. First they came into
exciting black darkness.

The little black kitten blinked his
bright green eyes in the darkness.
The little white kitten blinked two
little yellow eyes, and the little calico
kitten blinked his great big blue eyes.
For kittens can see in the dark.

The three little kittens crept ahead
until they came to some steps. The
steps were steep and hard to climb.
But, one by one, each little kitten
pulled himself up — step by step.

At the top of the steps was a long
crack of light. That was where the

little kittens were going. Beyond was
a kitchen full of good cooking smells.

Three little kitten heads came
peeking through the door. And there
was the most wonderful thing of all,
to kittens. Milk! There was a full
saucer of it, warm from the warmth
of the room. The little kittens drank
it so fast, they spattered it all over
their faces.

73

They were sitting under the stove, licking each other clean and dry, when they heard the big feet coming. They were great big feet, the biggest feet the kittens had ever seen. The feet came nearer. Two hands put a pie on the kitchen table. Then the feet went away.

It didn't take the three kittens long to climb right up on the table and sniff around the pie. Then the little black kitten pounced right into the middle of the pie, and squirted the red juice of it into the white kitten's eye. The little calico kitten just stood on the other side of the pie and waited, with his eyes shining. And when the little black kitten crawled out of the pie and onto the table, they grabbed him.

They grabbed the black kitten and gave him a good cat-scrubbing with their tongues.

Then the little black kitten went pouncing too near the edge of the table cloth, and fell. Down, down, he went, pulling the whole table cloth with him. Plates and pans came crashing down. The little white kitten slid down the table cloth like a shoot-the-chute. And the pie landed right on top of him.

The kittens liked the noise of the crash. It was such a big exciting noise. Then they licked themselves clean once more, and went off to explore the house.

In the dining room, they saw a feather blowing about in the air.

The black kitten began a dance with it. He jumped in the air and smacked it with his paw. The calico kitten danced, too. But it was the white kitten who discovered the hot air coming up through the grate in the floor. He put his paw in it. But the air blew right past him. He couldn't see what it was, but he knew that it was warm and soft and wonderful. He waved his paw in it back and forth, back and forth.

Then they discovered the piano. Ping pang! ping pang! — Kitten on the keys. The black kitten danced on the high notes, and the white kitten danced on the low notes.

At that, in came the two big feet.

And the two big feet chased the three little kittens all over the house.

Finally, the kittens ran upstairs and hid in the little girl's room. They hid in her closet, and each little kitten climbed into a shoe and went to sleep.

The little black kitten climbed into a soft red slipper and went to sleep. The other two kittens climbed into a pair of sneakers and went to sleep.

There they were when the little girl found them. They were all curled up in her shoes — three sleepy little soft angel kittens. And the little girl loved them and kept them forever. And the kittens thought the little girl was wonderful. Even the cook, who owned the big feet, grew to love the three little kittens.

THE FLYING MOUSE

There was once a mouse who longed
for wings, great big wonderful flying
things. He wanted to fly away
through the sky on great big wings
that would carry him high. He
wanted to be a flying mouse and fly
over everybody's house. He was tired
of being a little ground mouse.

And then one time in the middle of the night there came a bright light into his room. And a small voice said, "Little mouse, little mouse, get up and go to the place where the brook flows into the river. And from the second branch of the smallest tree pick two green leaves."

So the little mouse combed his whiskers and ran down to the place where the brook flows into the river. There was a little beech tree that grew there. And from the second branch the little mouse picked two green leaves.

"Now," said the mouse, "I have two green leaves. But what can a little mouse do with these?"

Then came the bright light again,

all over the river. And a small voice said:

"Little mouse, little mouse. Take the leaves you have there. Put them under your arms and fly through the air!"

And, lo and behold, the little mouse took the two green leaves and flew through the air.

And as he flew, the leaves became wings, great big wonderful flying things. And the little mouse began to fly. He flew over the houses of the other mouses.

He flew along with his wings up there. And he flew, and he flew, and he flew through the air. He flew over the treetops and everywhere.

Then he came down out of the air to play with the other mice. But when they saw him, they ran away. They were all afraid and would not play with a flying mouse.

Then the little mouse went to tease the cat. And the cat said, "Goodness! What is that?" And electricity flew out of his hair. "I can't chase a mouse up in the air."

The cat switched his tail like a lion
in its lair. Who ever saw a mouse
flying through the air! He would not
play with a flying mouse.

83

Then the mouse went to a rat to ask for some cheese. And the rat looked at his wings and said, "What are these? And why should I give a flying mouse cheese? I have no cheese for a flying mouse. Get out of my house!"

Then the mouse went calling on the

birds in the air. He waved his wings
and flew up there. And the birds all
fluttered, and one bird sang: "Little
flying mouse, you may have wings.
But we only play with feathered
things. We cannot play with a
flying mouse."

And then came on the dark black
night. The places he knew were out
of sight. And then he heard an awful
hiss.

"Heavens!" said the mouse. "Now
what is this?"

And there in the air, flying
everywhere, were terrible bats. They
looked like great black flying rats.
Bats!

The bats were glad to see the
mouse, and they flew with him into a
darkened house.

But the mouse was not very
pleased at that. A mouse will never
be pleased with a bat. The mouse
was not happy there in the dark with

the snarling bats, and the hiss and the squeak and the other sounds that black bats speak.

When morning came and he looked around, the bats were sleeping upside down. So the little mouse flew down to the ground. He flew to the ground and he ran to the brook. And in the water — he took one look!

"Oh, dear me! Now what is that?"

For the flying mouse looked like a little fat bat. And the little mouse did not like that.

Then the little mouse began to shiver, and he ran and he ran and he ran to the river. He sat down under the little beech tree. And he wondered and wondered what on earth he could be.

There was no place on earth for a flying mouse. He didn't want to live in the Black Bat House. And no one would play with a flying mouse.

"Oh dear me," said the little mouse. "How I wish I were like other mice!"

And, lo and behold, the light came back all over the river. The mouse's wings began to quiver. His wings flew back to be leaves on the tree. And the little mouse danced and cried with glee, "I am ME!"

And the small voice said, "Little mouse, little mouse. Go back to your house and be a mouse!"

THE OLD MILL

As the sun left the sky, the clouds
in the west were gold and gray. The
peace of evening came down over the
land.

The spider hurried to weave the last
strands of his web before dark. The
cows went slowly home across the
ridge of the hill. And the ducks
waddled into the barn.

The windmill stood with its giant ragged arms against the evening sky. Quietness came all around.

The blue barnswallow with the red breast swooped into the old mill. He carried in his beak a worm for his little mate who was keeping warm their three blue eggs. They were at home in the old mill. Their nest was made in a cog-hole of the mill stone. For the old mill had not been used for many years except as a home for birds and animals.

As darkness came on, the old fat owl who slept through the day opened his round yellow eyes. He cocked his head and stamped from one foot to the other. Then he called in a sleepy way, "Whoo! Whoo! Whoo!"

Farther up, bright eyes came out
like electric lights in the darkness
under the roof. These were the eyes
of the bats. For the bats lived in the
old mill, too, hanging upside down as
they slept through the day.

One bat after another unfolded its spreading wings and stretched them wide. And then the bats fluttered forth from the old mill like ragged scattered leaves.

Outside, the moon came up in a soft golden mist. The crickets began to chirp in the soft summer night.

On the pond, as the last of the water lilies closed, two big eyes peered from under a lily pad. And out jumped a big green bullfrog.

He jumped on a lily pad and croaked:

"Come! Come!
Come! Come!"

And another frog croaked:

"Come where?
Come where?
Come! Come!
Come where?"

Another frog answered:

"Come here!
Come where?
Come! Come!"

And yet another frog croaked:

"Come over there!
Come here!
Come where?
Come! Come!"

A great chorus of frogs was croaking on the lily pads of the pond.

Lightning bugs made hundreds of golden sparks in the darkness.

Then the wind began to blow. It swept through the trees. Great black clouds sailed over the moon. The wind blew harder. Leaves fell down from the trees into the pond, and the frogs dived under the water. Plop.

Then the storm came on in all its crashing fury.

The great arms of the windmill turned round and round and round in the wind.

The old fat owl sitting on a rafter above the water wheel inside the mill was nearly thrown from his perch. Water dripped on the fat owl's head and made him angry. He seemed to grow bigger and bigger as he ruffled up his feathers in anger.

Outside, the wind blew the trees low and blew down the fence posts. The slender reeds in the swamp broke off at their lower joints.

Then, in the fury of the storm, the rope that held the mill wheel broke! The arms of the old mill once more were free. They turned round and round against the sky, and the big wheel inside the mill began to turn.

The mother bird on her nest saw the great wheel coming down above her. She fluttered away from the nest in fright. Then she flew back and covered the nest with her wings. She did not know that the cog for that hole in the mill stone was broken. And so the big wheel came rolling over her nest and left her there unhurt.

Around and around, the great jagged arms of the windmill turned and turned against the sky. Black clouds went racing over the moon.

Lightning flashed in jagged cracks. And inside the mill the great wheel turned around and around over the little mother barnswallow.

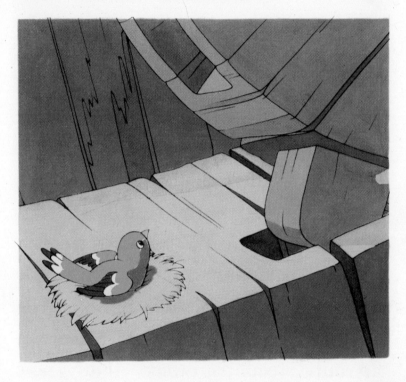

The wind shrieked outside but the little swallow never left her nest. She covered it and kept the eggs warm.

Lightning flashed close by the fat old owl, so that he moved sideways on his perch. Then he blinked and turned his head.

The lightning came again with a deafening crash. It struck the old mill and broke off one of the arms of the windmill. The old mill shook, and its turning wheel went slower.

The wind died down, and there was only the sound of the rain. And the sound of the rain grew softer and softer until it went away. Then the sky outside grew green and light in the east. The moon was gone. And the old mill stood as before. Only now one ragged arm was broken and hanging down against the morning sky.

All was peaceful, as though the
storm had never been. The wind and
lightning had come and gone. The
cows went slowly over the hill. The
ducks came out of the barn and swam
back to the green reeds by the edge of
the pond.

Inside the mill the old fat owl blinked and closed his eyes. And the bats came flying home.

In the nest under the mill wheel three little birds were opening yellow bills. And the mother and father swallow came flying in. They had worms for their baby birds who had been born in the storm. The blue feathers of the baby barnswallows were shining in the morning sun.

All was quiet as before. The storm had come and gone. And the sunlight was caught in the spider's web.

Date Due